635.9
Sel
c.1   Selsam, Millicent E.

         How to grow house plants

691075

How To Grow House Plants

How To Grow
House Plants

By MILLICENT E. SELSAM
Illustrated By Kathleen Elgin

WILLIAM MORROW AND COMPANY
New York . . 1960

To the Ellis family

· · · · ·

CONTENTS

How To Grow House Plants

CHAPTER 1

The Secret of the Green Thumb

How many times have you heard people say, "I can't make plants grow," or, "Everything I touch dies"? And how many times have you heard the opposite kind of thing? "She has a green thumb," or, "She has such wonderful luck with plants!" If you are one of these "green thumb" people, your plants are supposed to grow almost by magic! But the real secret of the green thumb is that there is no such thing. It isn't luck or magic that makes plants grow. It is knowledge of the conditions plants require and interest enough to provide them.

The plants we grow in our houses come from all over the world. Their natural homes may have been on the shady floors of steaming rain forests or in the upper branches of their tall trees. They might have come from hot dry deserts, from open fields, or from high mountain slopes. We take plants from such special environments and try to grow them in an average house or schoolroom, where conditions are very different. The air is as dry as a desert. The light is generally poor and comes from only one side. The temperature may be much too high. Either there is very little air or the room is too drafty. However, in spite of these difficulties, people are able to grow and enjoy house plants. They either choose plants that can stand the poor conditions in the home, or they change the conditions somewhat and make them reasonably good for a larger number of plants. You will find ways, in this book, to do both of these things. You will find that no schoolroom or home need be without the green beauty of growing plants.

Many people who grow house plants talk of them as if they were human beings and have thoughts and feelings. They say things like, "My plants hate drafts," or, "They look forward to their weekly shower," or, "These plants prefer not to have their roots disturbed." We must remember that plants do not have feelings and do not think or hate or want anything. You can look in vain for any sign of a brain in a plant that would make it able to do these things. A plant consists only of root, stem, and leaves.

The diagram shows the main function of these different parts of the plant. The root anchors the plant and takes in water and minerals from the soil. Thousands of tiny delicate root hairs extend out from the surface of the root into the

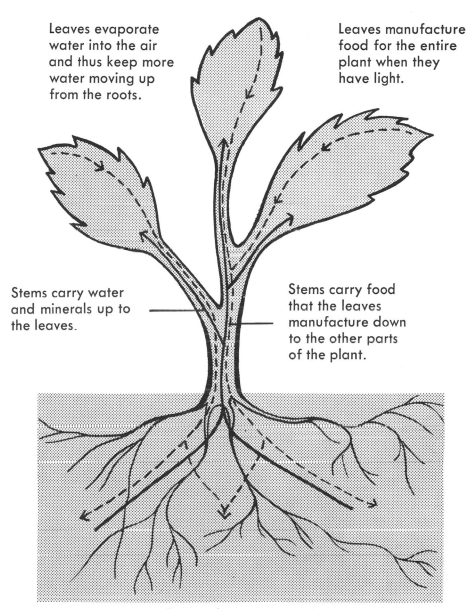

Leaves evaporate water into the air and thus keep more water moving up from the roots.

Leaves manufacture food for the entire plant when they have light.

Stems carry water and minerals up to the leaves.

Stems carry food that the leaves manufacture down to the other parts of the plant.

Roots take in water and minerals from the soil.

soil. The water and minerals pass through their thin cell walls into the center of the root and from there up the stem through special long, thin, woody vessels. By the time the water with its dissolved minerals reaches the leaves, it is traveling through tiny vessels or veins, and from these it passes into the green cells of the leaf.

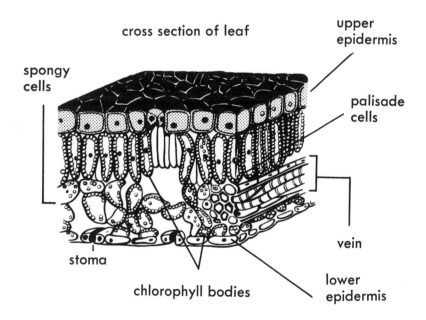

cross section of leaf

upper epidermis

spongy cells

palisade cells

vein

stoma

chlorophyll bodies

lower epidermis

A cross section of a leaf shows its simple structure. There is a thin protective layer (epidermis) on top and bottom. The cells between these two layers are surrounded by air spaces that have a connection to the outside air through little pores (stomata) in the underside of the leaf. Most of the leaf cells are green, because they contain small round bodies called chloroplasts that are full of a green substance called chlorophyll. The green cells of the leaf are the "factories" that manufacture food for the entire plant. Incidentally, they produce food for us, too, because we eat plants, and animals that feed on plants.

Light supplies the energy for this food-making process, which is called photosynthesis. The raw materials are the water drawn up from the soil, and the carbon dioxide of the air that passes in through the leaf pores. These two substances are combined to form simple sugars.

The sugars travel down through special tubes in the outer ring of the stem to all parts of the plant, where they are combined with minerals from the soil. They are changed into such foods as oils, proteins, and other substances necessary to plant life and growth.

A plant, then, has a root system which takes the water and minerals from the soil, a stem in which water and minerals travel up and food sugars travel down, and leaves which act like chemical factories producing the basic sugars that all the cells of the plant use. Once you understand the make-up of a plant, as it has just been described, the directions for taking care of your house plants will make sense. To carry on their basic activities, plants need water, light, minerals, air, and a proper temperature. No green thumb and no amount of luck will take the place of knowing these simple requirements of plants and providing them.

CHAPTER 2

Water for Your Plants

A plant cannot live without water. Water enters into almost every activity that goes on in the plant. It keeps the cells plump and the whole plant upright and firm. Without it, a plant droops, gets limp, and finally wilts. The mineral salts in the soil can enter the plant only when they are dissolved in water. Water is necessary for all the plant's food-making activities, for transport of all materials, and for the growth of new roots, stems, and leaves.

The interesting thing is that nearly all the water absorbed by the roots of plants evaporates into the surrounding air. There is a constant stream of water going from the roots, through the stem, and into the cells of the leaf. But it doesn't stay there. It evaporates through the walls of the leaf cells and, as water vapor, passes out into the air through the leaf pores. Some water also evaporates through the walls of the epidermis.

If this water were visible, you could see it surrounding the plant like a fine mist.

water vapor around plant

The constant evaporation from the leaf cells means that the stream of water in the thin water-carrying tubes of the plant must keep rising from roots to leaves. With all this water being constantly given off by the leaves, there must be enough in the soil to enter the roots and replace it.

There can be only general rules about watering plants, because they have such different requirements. Plants with large thin leaves lose water very rapidly, and the soil in which these plants are growing must never be allowed to get completely dry. Other plants, with thick rubbery leaves, or plants like the cactus, do not lose water rapidly. These plants have to be

16

watered much less often, and the soil can be allowed to dry between waterings.

One general rule is to water your plants only when the top soil feels dry. Or you can pinch a bit of the soil in your fingers, and if it sticks together when squeezed, do not water the plants. If it falls apart, however, be sure to water them.

A second general rule is to water thoroughly when you find the soil dry. Don't just sprinkle some water on the top. Add water until you see it seeping out through the hole in the bottom of the flowerpot. Then don't water again until the top

Light sprinkling waters only to here. The rest stays dry.   Thorough watering soaks contents of pot throughout.

soil feels dry. The trick is to keep the soil moist but not too wet. Lots of plants are ruined by too much watering. Excess water fills the air spaces between the particles of soil and deprives the roots of the air which they need in order to function. Without air, a root decays.

17

The containers you are using for your plants will make a lot of difference in the amount of water you have to supply. Clay pots with holes at the bottom are the easiest to use, because excess water runs out, and some water evaporates from the sides of the pot. If you use glass or glazed containers without holes at the bottom, you should put in a bottom layer of pebbles or stones one half to one inch thick, depending on the size of the container, into which the excess water can run off. Water plants in such containers carefully until you learn to judge how much water is needed just to moisten the soil and not soak it.

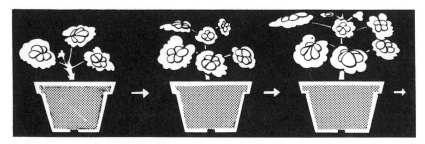

Plants growing actively need more water.

rest period

Many of our house plants go through a rest period in the winter. At this time, when the tempo of a plant's activities is slowed down, water sparingly. In the spring, house plants come to life and do most of their growing for the year. When you see a plant starting to grow actively—when it puts out new leaves and shoots and buds and its stems begin to lengthen —it will need lots of water.

Moisture in the Air

The average house using a steam heating system in the winter has air about as dry as a desert. Cacti can thrive in such dry air and, for this reason, make very good and dependable house plants. But if you want to grow other kinds of plants, something must be done to increase the moisture, or humidity, in the air.

There are several ways to do this. The best way is to provide shallow trays filled with pebbles on which you can stand your plants. If you have just a few plants, set the pots on a layer of pebbles in a baking pan, or cooky tin, a plastic tray, or any other shallow container. If you want to have a good collection of plants, have a tray made to fit the size of the window sill that gets the most light. Such trays are made very cheaply by tinsmiths from galvanized iron or aluminum. They should

keeping the air around plants moist

be the same length and width as the sill, and two inches high. Add water up to the top layer of pebbles and keep the water at that level at all times. The water will evaporate from the surface and keep the air around the plants moist. Evaporation takes place in direct proportion to the surface area of the evaporating liquid. That is why having water spread out in shallow trays does so much good, while deep containers hung on radiators do so little good.

Shallow trays automatically increase the humidity around your plants in another way. Since each plant gives off a lot of water vapor, grouping your plants in one place makes the air over them moister than anywhere else in the room.

If you want to keep a few plants in a large box, or planter, fill the space between the pots with moist peat that can be kept damp. Spraying the leaves of your plants with water also helps a great deal. For this purpose, you can buy a sprayer with a fine-mist nozzle, or you can use a Windex bottle, or any other bottle that has a sprayer. If you have large plants, placed where they can't be sprayed, wipe their leaves with a moist sponge.

Using pebble trays, grouping your plants, and spraying them occasionally will do much to overcome the chief difficulty in growing house plants—the dryness of the air during the winter.

CHAPTER 3

Light for Your Plants

Plants need light so that their leaves can manufacture food for the entire plant. For this reason, we generally place our plants where they will get the greatest possible amount of light. But some plants do not need as much light as others. As a rule, foliage plants (those cultivated for their leaves) do well in less light than flowering plants, which need sunlight.

If the window you are planning to use faces south, you will have sun for many hours of the day. An east or west window will give you sunlight for a few hours a day. A north window will give you light but no sun. Select the plants suited to the location you want to use.

In a north window you can grow many foliage plants. Start with some of the ivies, such as English ivy and grape ivy. Try philodendron, the snake plant, the Swiss cheese plant, rubber plants, palms, Chinese evergreen, African evergreen, the spider

north window plants

plant, the cast-iron plant, and various ferns.

An east or west window can be the site for begonias, palms, lemon and orange plants, African violets, caladium, and the asparagus fern.

All the plants that grow well in an east or west window are suited to a south window. But in a south window you can also grow cactus, coleus, crotons, and a great many flowering plants such as the geranium, the narcissus, etc.

You can tell whether or not your plants are getting enough

23

east and west window plants

light. Those that aren't turn pale green, the stems and leaf stalks get very long, and the whole plant becomes too tall and gets a leggy appearance.

You will notice that plants kept on your window sill constantly bend their stems and leaves toward the light. This positive response to light is an advantage to the plant, because the leaves always take a position in which the broad surface of the leaf blade is at right angles to the light rays. In this way they receive the greatest light energy for the food-manufacturing process. But if you never turn your plants, they will get a

24

south window plants

lopsided look, and their beauty will be facing the wrong way —toward the outside where nobody sees them. So keep turning your plants around every few days.

Plants respond to light.

Rays of Light

Sunlight is made up of lots of colors which you can see only when light passes through a prism. In the prism, the white light is broken up into the colors of the rainbow. We see a spectrum, or series of colors, starting with short violet rays at one end and going from blue to green to yellow to orange to red (the longest rays we see). Beyond this spectrum there are rays we do not see—ultraviolet rays (shorter than the violet) and infrared radiations (longer than the red rays).

Which of these rays does the plant use? We know that ultraviolet rays do not pass through ordinary glass windows. Yet we grow our plants on window sills and behind the glass walls of greenhouses. Ultraviolet rays, then, are of no use to the plant. Experiments have shown that the plant uses the red and blue rays of white light in the process of manufacturing its food.

Artificial Light

This knowledge has led to the use of artificial light from ordinary electric light bulbs and fluorescent bulbs for growing plants. The light from such bulbs has red and blue rays and can meet all the needs of a plant. If your available daylight is insufficient, try supplementing it with electric light. You can keep foliage plants growing under wall lamps and under the light of table lamps if you use sixty-or seventy-five-watt bulbs. Plants must be kept about two feet away from ordinary light bulbs, because they give off so much heat.

garden under fluorescent light

If you like you can set up a miniature garden in any dark corner of your house by using fluorescent lighting. Any recess in a wall, or an empty cabinet, china closet, bookcase, or table top can be made into a growing area for plants. The simplest

27

setup consists of two forty-watt fluorescent lamps mounted in a fixture over a growing area about three feet wide and four feet long. The lamps can come down to within a foot of the plants. The lights have to be kept on for about fifteen hours a day, but the cost of the electricity will come to only a little extra per month.

The Length of Day

Recent discoveries in plant science have shown that the length of time which light lasts is also important to plants. Day length affects the flowering of some plants very greatly. We all know that in the short days of springtime we see forsythia and violets flower. Then the day lengthens and by midsummer we see gladiolus and other summer-flowering plants. In the fall, when days grow shorter, chrysanthemums bloom. All these plants are responding to the right balance, for them, between day and night. Plant scientists worked on this problem of day length and soon found that chrysanthemums could be made to bloom at any time of year as long as they were subjected to short days and long nights. They became known as short-day plants. But they really should have been called long-night plants, because if their long night is interrupted by even a minute of light, they will not flower.

28

Nurserymen can supply flower stores with chrysanthemums all year round now, simply because they control the periods of light and dark to which the plants are subjected. You can buy gladioli all year round, too, because gladiolus plants are given long-day and short-night treatment and made to flower.

You can see the effect of day length on some of your house plants. Poinsettia and Christmas cactus will not flower until the days get short in the winter season. Other house plants do not start to bloom until the spring and summer, when the days are longer. And some are not affected too much by day length, but bloom all year round.

CHAPTER 4

Inside a Flowerpot

The soil in a flowerpot does three things for a plant. It anchors the roots. It provides the plant with water and mineral salts necessary to its growth. And it allows air to reach the roots.

Ordinary soil can be used in flowerpots, but with frequent watering it will pack down hard and prevent the water from running off freely. For this reason, house plants are usually potted in a mixture of ordinary soil, sand, and humus. The sand is added to keep the soil loose so that water can drain off. But it is not desirable for the water to drain off too quickly, so humus is added too. Humus is the dark brown or black part of the soil that comes from the decayed remains of plants —dead leaves, stems, and roots—or from parts of dead animals or the dung of animals. The humus helps to hold water in the soil and improves its texture by loosening it and admitting air.

If you have your own garden and want to mix your own potting soil, combine two parts of garden soil with one part humus and one part sand. You can get your humus from a compost pile of dead leaves, or you can buy peat or commercial humus. Peat comes from decomposed swamp plants, while commercial humus comes from leaves and stems that have decayed in woods or around the edges of lakes.

But the easiest and most sensible way to get a good potting soil, especially if you live in the city, is to buy the new ready-mixed, sterilized, packaged potting soils. They contain the garden soil, sand, and humus in proper proportion, and save a lot of time and mess. They are all-purpose mixtures which

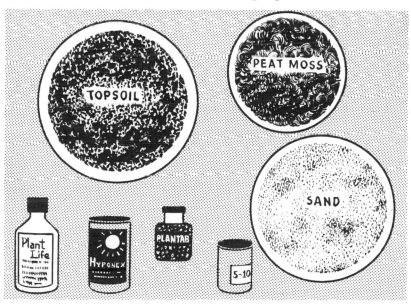

31

can be used for most house plants. Some house plants do have special requirements, but these are easily taken care of. Plants like African violets, ferns, and begonias do well with more than the usual proportion of humus (two parts garden soil, two parts humus, one part sand). Such special mixtures, rich in humus, are available in packages too. They are generally labeled African Violet Soil. Desert types of plants, like cactus, do better with soil containing a higher proportion of sand (two parts soil, two parts humus, two parts sand).

Plants should be kept in pots just big enough to enable them to grow. If the pots are too big, the soil in them will easily be overwatered, because there are not enough roots to absorb the water.

The time will come when a plant should be moved from a small pot to a slightly larger one, because the plant roots have entirely filled the pot. To see if a plant needs repotting, turn the pot upside down, hold the stem of the plant between your fingers, and rap the rim against a hard surface. This will loosen the ball of earth in the pot, and the whole thing will slide forward into your hand. If the roots completely fill the earth ball so that no soil can be removed from the surface, it is time to repot. Use a pot about one inch larger than the old one.

To prevent the soil from clogging up the hole at the bottom

repotting

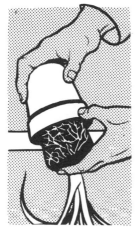

Rap rim of pot. Loosen ball of earth. Cover hole of new pot with pot chips.

Place plant in new soil of pot. Fill fresh soil in around roots. cross section of newly planted pot.

of the new pot, cover the hole with a piece of broken flower-pot. If the pot is small, one piece is enough. If it is big, a layer of flowerpot chips or pebbles about one inch thick should be added. The chips will allow the water to escape easily from the bottom of the pot. If you are using flowerpots without drainage holes, fill the bottom fourth of the pot with pebbles or flowerpot chips. Put a little fresh soil into the pot, place the plant on it, and fill fresh soil in around the roots.

After the plant has been repotted, rap the pot several times to settle the soil. Leave a half inch space at the top of the pot for watering. Then water thoroughly, until water runs out through the bottom of the pot.

Fertilizer for House Plants

Many people are surprised to find out that house plants have to be fed! If a plant makes it own food, why do we have to feed it? The answer is that plants make their own sugars with water from the soil and carbon dioxide from the air. But they cannot manufacture protoplasm, cell walls, chlorophyll, and other plant parts. In other words, they cannot grow unless certain chemical elements are dissolved in the water of the soil in which they are rooted.

Many elements enter into the life of a plant, but the three

most important of these are nitrogen, phosphorus, and potassium. You can find these "big three" in any fertilizer you buy. Nitrogen makes leaves and stems grow. Phosphorus fosters flower, fruit, and seed. Potassium stiffens the stems and promotes sturdy, compact growth.

A plant just brought home from a nursery or a florist doesn't need any fertilizer for several months, because the potting soil that was used contains enough phosphorus, potassium, and nitrogen to last that long. But after a few months, if the plant has grown and the pot has become crowded with roots, additional minerals must be added to the soil. The easiest fertilizers to use for indoor plants are the liquid fertilizers. Follow the manufacturer's directions carefully, for too much fertilizer can burn the roots of a plant.

Plants that are growing actively should be fertilized about every three weeks. In the winter, when most house plants are in a resting state, do not add plant food.

Fertilizers have always been added to soil, because it was thought that minerals could only be absorbed through the roots. But it has been proved recently that liquid fertilizer can be sprayed on leaves and will be absorbed and used by the entire plant. Try leaf feedings on philodendrons, the Swiss cheeese plant, and any other jungle-type plants that have shallow roots but many leaves.

Since the food a plant gets from the soil consists of water and the minerals dissolved in it, it is easy to understand why plants can be grown without soil—in plain water to which minerals have been added. This is the new science of hydroponics, or soilless growth of plants, and it is used extensively now to grow crops where land is not available.

CHAPTER 5

Plants for the Beginner

There are quite a number of house plants that are "tough" in the sense that they will live and grow in spite of dry air, drafts, poor light, and even neglect. The beginner should start with these. Many of them are not only tough but lovely. You can select plants that have dramatic silhouettes, unusual leaf shapes, markings and veinings, stems and leaves with different tones of green, and many other interesting characteristics.

You can buy these plants from five-and-tens, florists, or nurseries. Select hardy *young* plants so that you can have the fun of watching them grow. Below is a description of several of these tough house plants, and a list in the back of the book gives their scientific names. All these plants will thrive with ordinary care. If you are successful with them, you can go on to all sorts of special plants.

Portraits of Some Plant "Toughies"

The snake plant is a well known "toughie." Every shoe store, barbershop, and laundry is pretty sure to have one of these plants in its window. The common kinds have stiff, long, pointed leaves striped with yellow or gray. This plant is really hard to kill.

The spider plant has grass-like leaves that grow out in rosettes, and small white flowers. Its charm lies in the fact that it produces long runners along which new plantlets that look like little spiders grow. You can put this plant in a hanging basket and allow the runners to droop over the edge.

The cast-iron plant rightly deserves its name, for it withstands the most difficult conditions. Every Victorian parlor used to have one of these plants, but it can be very attractive in modern homes, too, with its long leaves springing in a cluster directly from the soil. It will grow very well in a window that has no sunshine and can be used for long periods to brighten up a dim corner.

The rubber plant is an old-time favorite. The only special care it needs is an occasional washing of the leaves. The new fiddle-leaf rubber plants have leaves of bold design and are very much used in modern homes.

39

Chinese evergreen grows in soil or plain water. If water is used, some liquid fertilizer should be added every few weeks. This plant comes from Asian jungles, where it grows on the forest floor. It can grow in dim light.

Philodendron could easily win a plant popularity contest. Practically every home has one of these plants. The ones with heart-shaped leaves are the most familiar, but there are actually about 300 kinds of philodendron. Its name comes from *philo,* meaning love, and *dendron,* meaning tree. It was given to these plants, because in their tropical home in the jungles of South America they climb up the trunks of tall trees. Roots sprout out from the stems as they grow. These aerial roots should be kept sprayed with water and an occasional dose of liquid fertilizer. Philodendron needs light, but not full sunlight. It can be grown in plain water as well as soil. If grown in water, it will need some liquid fertilizer every few weeks.

The Swiss cheese plant has huge leaves that look as though they were cut into with a pair of scissors. It gets its name from the fact that it is perforated with holes, like Swiss cheese. In its native Central America and Mexico, it climbs the trees much as philodendron does, by aerial roots. The plant should be kept away from drafts and its large leaves

should be washed often. Its aerial roots should be treated like those of the philodendron.

English ivy is well known to everyone. It grows best in a cool situation, so pick the coolest window available. The leaves should be frequently sprayed with water, to avoid the mites that often attack them. It can be grown in plain water, too, if occasionally fertilized. Another common ivy, grape ivy, is hardy and needs no special treatment. It has shiny tripatted leaves, like poison ivy.

42

Wandering Jew makes a good hanging-basket plant that is easy to care for. The small leaves may be plain green, or striped, or have purple undersides. These plants can also be grown in water, if an occasional dose of fertilizer is added.

The screw pine has long swordlike leaves edged with sharp spines. The leaves are arranged spirally and give the plant an interesting outline, useful in modern *décor*.

The Australian umbrella tree is a rather new house plant. It resembles a tree, and has clusters of shiny leaves, like leafy umbrellas. It grows slowly and needs very little attention in spite of its beauty.

43

African evergreen bears this name, even though the plant is a native of Central America and the West Indies. Florists call it nephthytis. It can be grown in plain water like the Chinese evergreen. In some varieties, its arrow-shaped leaves are streaked with white.

Fatshedera is a new house plant that comes from a cross between an English ivy (Hedera) and a Japanese plant called fatsia. Its name shows the combination too. Its leaves are larger and more beautiful than those of English ivy. This plant can grow in poor light.

Dumb cane gets its name from the fact that the stems, if chewed, cause temporary dumbness, or loss of speech. The calcium-oxalate crystals in the stems paralyze the tongue. The leaves are large and striking and may be splotched with white or yellow. The plant should be given warmth and good light but not direct sunlight.

The **corn plant is so named** because it resembles the corn that grows in the field. Water this plant freely. It does not require direct sunlight.

Cacti are the easiest plants to grow in the average home, provided there is a window available that gets several hours of sunlight a day. These plants can

stand the desert dryness of a steam-heated home very well, because their fleshy stems store water and the thick skin prevents evaporation. You can have great fun picking out strange forms and shapes from the 1300 different kinds of cactus available. The soil should be kept on the dry side. During the winter, when cacti are in a resting stage, watering once a week is enough.

cacti

Succulents are a group of plants that resemble cacti, because they, too, have thick fleshy stems and fleshy leaves that store

succulents

watcr. On page 48 are a few of the many succulents you can find. All of them need a sandy soil kept on the dry side, and as much sun as possible.

The jade plant looks like a miniature tree with rubbery leaves.

The aloe, from the deserts of Africa, has a stiff outline of pointed leaves edged with soft spines.

Echeveria or hen and chickens has rosettes of leaves that are often gray green and blue green. New little plants form "chickens" around the "hen" plant.

Kalanchoe has many species, but the most familiar is the little green one that is covered with bright red flowers in winter.

Bryophyllum is a succulent you find in the five-and-tens being sold under the name air plant or miracle leaf, because tiny little plants form around the margins of the leaf when it is detached from the plant.

Sedum or live-forever can be found in most rock gardens and can grow indoors quite well.

Crown of thorns has large, sharp, dark spines and tiny flowers with bright scarlet bracts (leaves) under them.

Bromeliads are an easy-to-grow group of plants in the pineapple family. Most of these plants have stiff rosettes of leaves like the pineapple, and exotic flowers combining blues, reds, and greens. They are natives of Central and South American jungles, where many of them perch in the crotches of tall trees. The overlapping leaves of the rosettes form leaf cups that hold water. Water and minerals enter the plant through these cups as well as through the roots. For this reason, keep the leaf cups filled with water. They grow well in east, west, or south windows. These plants can be placed in the crevices of driftwood. Find natural holes and cut them deeper. Wrap the roots in sphagnum moss, press them into the cavities, and tie them in place. After a while, the plants will take hold, and you can remove the ties.

bromeliads

CHAPTER 6

Miniature Gardens

A miniature garden can be made in a dish. It can be a woodland scene, a desert landscape, a tropical jungle, a water garden, or any scene you would like to reproduce on a small scale. A pebble can look like a rock, a rock like a mountain, a tiny pool like a lake, a seedling tree like a forest giant. It all depends on how you arrange your material.

First search your home for a suitable container. Is there a pottery bowl or casserole or glass dish with a depth between four and six inches available? Or can you find a metal container of copper or brass or iron? These can be used if they are lined with aluminum foil. An old pot, a kettle, or a baking tin can be used, too, and even coconut shells and scooped-out turnips can become containers for dish gardens.

Dish-garden culture is simple if you follow a few basic rules. Good drainage is an absolute necessity. If your container

50

plant containers

has drainage holes in the bottom, that is fine, But if it doesn't, put an inch-thick layer of pebbles or charcoal bits at the bottom of a shallow container (three to four inches), and a two-inch layer at the bottom of deeper ones. The purpose of this layer is to hold excess water that drains out of the soil. This will prevent the soil above it from getting soggy. Even so, you have to be careful about your watering. Try to add just enough to keep the soil moist but not wet, and water again only when the soil in the container is no longer damp to the touch.

The second requirement for dish gardening is a porous soil

that can hold plenty of air and water. You have to avoid heavy clay soils that pack down hard after a few waterings and prevent air from reaching the roots. Since roots decay when they have no access to air, select a light spongy soil rich in humus. You can use a packaged soil like Black Magic, or African Violet Soil. If you like, you can make a half and half mixture of garden soil and peat moss. Perlite and vermiculite are two new materials you can use to lighten soil. Perlite is a white porous material that comes from volcanic rock. Vermiculite is mica ore. Both of these materials are heated until they pop into smaller spongy particles that hold both air and many times their weight in water. Mix these with soil to get a light spongy consistency.

With a light soil and provision for drainage, you are ready for your plants. Here you must follow another rule. Group together only those plants that have similar requirements. You cannot put cactus plants into a dish with jungle and tropical plants and expect to keep them both alive. What will be just enough water for tropicals will mean death to the cactus. Plants that grow naturally together will be the best for you to group together in a dish.

Plan your dish garden before you start on it. Make a rough sketch of the arrangement you want to have. If you want to keep the dish against a wall, visible from only one side, put the taller plants in the back, or mound the soil higher toward the back of the dish. If it is to be seen from all sides, center the taller plants and put smaller ones toward the edges. Choose slow-growing plants, because you won't want your plants to outgrow the dish garden quickly.

Desert Dish Garden

A desert dish garden is ideal for a hot dry room and requires very little care. But you must have direct sunlight available for several hours each day. Your desert dish garden can be put in a container as small as a teacup, or it can spread out and fill a whole metal tray on your window sill. Add half sand to whatever soil mixture you are planning to use for dish gardens. If you can't find sand easily, crush and crumble a few flowerpots and use these fragments instead.

The plants you place in your desert garden should be cacti

desert garden

or succulents (see pp. 45, 46). You can combine interesting textures, colors, and shapes from the many different kinds available. Some resemble tall columns; others resemble round barrels, stones, rocks, or even pincushions. They may have spines of red or gold or purple, or hairs of different shades.

The care of the dish garden is easy. It has only to be watered about twice a week, when the plants are growing actively. When they are in the resting stage (usually in the winter) they only need to be watered once a week.

It is easy to make your desert dish garden look like a scene from the Arizona desert. Just carve out a doorway and window in a wooden block or two, as shown in the picture, and you will have the suggestion of Indian huts. Place your cacti and succulents, sprinkle a layer of sand about one half inch thick over the surface, and you will complete your scene.

Tropical Garden

You can have a miniature jungle in a dish if you have a glass fish bowl or aquarium that can be covered to help retain moisture. Put in a layer of pebbles first, for drainage. Then add the soil. You can choose from philodendron, ivy, small palms, ferns, Chinese evergreen, African violet, African evergreen, or any other small plants that have interesting markings

tropical garden

or colors. Water the soil so that it keeps moist but not soggy. Frequently spray the plants with water from a spray bottle or bulb spray. Keep the dish in bright light but not in direct sunlight. Design it, if you wish, with a small path of sand running through a mass of plants. If you keep a glass lid on, moisture will evaporate from the soil and plants and drip down on the foliage, giving the garden a jungly look. Prop the glass lid so that some air can enter, too, to prevent mildew and rot. Pieces of eraser or slivers of wood can be glued to the lid so that it will rest about one quarter of an inch above the rim. Plastic Saran Wrap can also be used for a lid, if you punch a few holes in it. With such a lid, this garden will practically water itself.

Woodland Garden

A woodland garden can also be planted in a fish bowl or

aquarium. Prepare it with pebbles and soil, just as you did for the tropical garden. But for plant material, take a walk through a woods. There you will find mosses, tiny little evergreen trees, sprouting acorns, small ferns, partridgeberries, and wintergreen in the fall. In the spring you will find small clumps of violets, hepaticas, and other small flowering woodland plants that carpet the forest floor. Don't crowd or jumble the plants together. Place them so that your container really looks like a miniature woodland. Use rocks, stones, pieces of bark, twigs, and branches to add interest. Provide this garden with a lid as described for the jungle garden, and this garden, too, will water itself.

woodland garden

Water Garden

A water garden can be made from plants specially adapted

to growing in water: Chinese evergreen, African evergreen, ivy, philodendron, wandering Jew, and coleus (its leaves have bright splashes of pink or red). Use a shallow container with a flower holder to keep the plants in place. Put in a few small pieces of charcoal, which helps to keep the water clear by absorbing impurities.

You can create an island of plants surrounded by water, or you can have a bank of plants bordering a circular pool. A tiny figure of a duck or a swan would complete the illusion. Keep the water level just above the roots and add liquid plant food, instead of water, about every two weeks. For a beautiful effect, place a narcissus bulb or autumn crocus bulb among the green plants of your water garden. If you have some good-sized stones of interesting shape, you can add them to make attractive rock and water combinations.

water garden

Kitchen Gardens

Many wonderful dish gardens can be made from your own kitchen fruits, vegetables, and seeds. Use pebbles for drainage, as you did before, and then add soil. Plant combinations of lentils and beans, from the packages of dried beans and lentils you buy in the grocery. Or grow each alone in a solid mass and set the dish on the kitchen or dining-room table. Just soak the seeds in water overnight, and then plant them beneath a quarter inch of soil.

lentils

Cut off the leafy top of a pineapple, where it is attached to the fruit. Allow the cut end to dry for a day or two, then plant it in the center of a dish garden. Around it you can place top pieces of carrot and let them sprout into a ring of lacy

pineapple and carrot tops

growth around the rosette of stiff pineapple leaves. To plant the carrot, trim off the old leaves, cut off the upper two inches (the wide end) and place it cut end down, one inch deep in soil, in the dish. The top pieces of turnips and beets and parsnips grow equally as well as those of carrots, and in the same way.

A dishful of orange, lemon, or grapefruit seedlings is a beautiful sight. To plant, take seeds from fruit that has plenty of seeds. The occasional seeds you find in seedless oranges, grapefruits, and lemons are not likely to grow well. Soak the

grapefruit

59

seeds overnight and then plant them about a quarter inch deep in your dish garden. They will sprout into a miniature forest of green, glossy-leaved fruit trees.

A large turnip or rutabaga will make a dish garden. Scoop out the center from the root end, leaving a shell one inch thick. Put soil into the hollow. Then plant lentil seeds, pea seeds, or any other kitchen seeds and cover with a quarter inch of soil. Set the turnip on a shallow dish of moist peat moss or vermiculite. Keep the soil in the hollow of the turnip as well as the material in the dish moist. From the base of the turnip, leaves will grow out and up, while the seeds in the center part will sprout into lentil plants, pea plants, or whatever you planted.

turnip dish garden

If you use a coconut shell as a container, saw off about one third of the coconut and scoop the meat out of the deep part. Fill with soil, to within an inch of the top, and plant any

coconut garden

fruit or vegetable seed in the soil. Then cement the coconut shell to a tile to keep it from toppling over. If you like, you can place the shell in a plant bracket small enough to suspend it. If you plan to use the coconut this way, plant sweet-potato eyes, or buds, in the soil. They will grow into vines and trail out over the coconut shell.

You can plant a wonderful and useful kitchen garden of herbs in an old casserole. Combine small pots of marjoram, thyme, peppermint, parsley, chives, or basil, and fill the spaces between the pots with damp peat moss or vermiculite. You can buy the plants or grow them yourself from seed.

Other Miniature Gardens

Use the directions in this chapter just to get started. Then let your imagination roam. Search out the new miniature varieties of geraniums and roses, which can add charm to any dish garden. See if you can make one plant look like a garden-in-itself. Perhaps a plant with long narrow leaves placed next to a pool in a dish garden will give the illusion of tall grass growing near a pond. Perhaps you can make one date palm look like an oasis scene in a desert by making a clay model of a pyramid in scale to stand next to it.

With a little creative planning, you can make your container gardens a great source of pleasure.

CHAPTER 7

Plant Housekeeping

A good plant housekeeper (or house-plant keeper) maintains a close watch on his plants. All yellow leaves, dead flowers, and broken stems are promptly removed. Large dusty leaves are washed off with a sponge. Small-leaved plants are sprayed with a fine water spray daily and given an occasional wash in the kitchen sink. This accomplishes three things. It cleans the leaves, adds humidity, and, most important of all, keeps down insect pests.

Insect Pests

The insects that appear most often on house plants are plant lice, mealy bugs, scale insects, white flies, and red-spider mites, shown on the next page. If you get the habit of looking

63

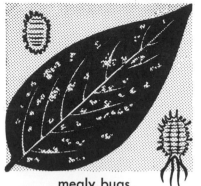

mealy bugs

scale insects

white flies

red-spider mites

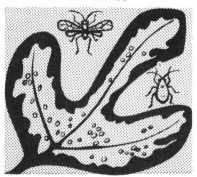

plant lice

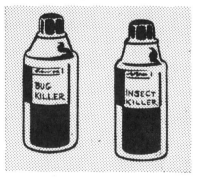

insecticide bombs

very closely at the undersides of leaves and at stem joints and the centers of rosettes of leaves, you can spot such insect troubles early and get rid of them easily. All these insects cause trouble, because they suck the plant juices. As a result, leaves turn yellow or spotty and growth is slowed down.

Plant lice are generally found clustered at the tips of young growing shoots. Masses of white cottony tufts are a sign that the mealy bugs are around. Their eggs are laid in this cotton. The scale insects look like tiny shiny oval lumps on stems and leaves. White flies cling to the undersides of leaves, and fly away in clouds when they are disturbed. They soon come back, however. Red-spider mites are almost too tiny to see with the naked eye. But if you notice fine webs at the tips of branches or under the leaves, you can be sure this insect is present. Regular spraying or washing of the leaves is the best preventive for red-spider mites, as well as all the other insects mentioned here. If you have real trouble with any of these pests and cannot keep them down by the washing routine, you can turn to the newest house-plant insect sprays for help. These are all-purpose insecticide aerosol bombs, and they combat all kinds of house-plant insect pests. Follow the manufacturer's directions carefully.

Air

A good plant housekeeper makes sure that air is allowed into the room where house plants are growing, but sees to it that no drafts blow directly on the plants. Plants do not need fresh air in the same sense that we do, since they are constantly producing oxygen as a by-product of photosynthesis. But fresh air does bring in humidity and helps to get rid of gas fumes that may have accumulated if artificial cooking gas is used.

cultivating the soil

The roots in the ground do need air, however. That is why good potting soil is loose and spongy, with lots of air spaces. If the top surface soil around a plant should happen to get caked and hard, use an old fork to loosen it up and admit air.

Temperature

Sudden changes of temperature may cause plants to drop their leaves. If you have to change the temperature of the room in which plants are growing, try to make the change gradually. Also, don't take plants from a warm room and put them outside to get watered by rain if it is cool outdoors. If you buy a plant at a greenhouse on a winter day, see that it is well wrapped with paper to protect it from the cold. The shift from a warm greenhouse to freezing temperatures can ruin the plant before it gets to your house.

Avoid extremes of temperature. Don't grow your plants over hot radiators unless you have a thick asbestos pad between the radiator and your plant tray. Temperatures next to windowpanes are colder than elsewhere in a room. On very cold nights, put several thicknesses of newspaper between your plants and the windowpane.

The Shape of Plants

Plants do not have to look lanky and scraggly. You can clip and trim a plant occasionally to keep its shape the way you want it. If you cut off the top bud of a plant, it forces the side buds to grow out and makes the plant more compact. The top bud produces a hormone that prevents the growth of the other buds below it. As soon as this bud is removed, the hormone is no longer present to inhibit the growth of the side buds.

pinching the top bud

side buds growing

A plant with top-heavy growth may need some support in the form of a stake. Use a support such as twigs or bamboo sticks (from the florist) that blend in with the growth. Fasten the plant to the stake as inconspicuously as possible. Use soft string or wool, and tie it loosely.

Some house plants are vines and need something to climb

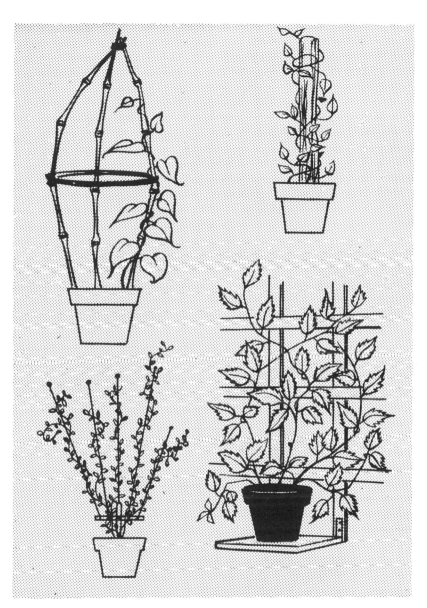

Some plants need support

on. You can make your own trellis of bamboo sticks tied together in the way shown in the picture. Twining plants like morning-glories need strings to climb on. These can be stretched from the end of a notched stick in the pot to a nail as high up as you want it. Plants like philodendron and ivy, which put out roots along the climbing stems, need supports of rough bark or cork. These supports should be sprayed with water daily to keep the aerial roots fresh.

Plant Doctoring

A good plant housekeeper has to be something of a plant doctor. If a plant is sickly-looking, with lots of yellow leaves, check to see whether it is being subjected to cold or drafts, or whether the soil in the pot has been kept too dry or too wet. Cold and drafts are fairly easy to stop. If you think the plant has been overwatered, stop watering, check the pot to see that the drainage material is still in operating condition, cultivate the soil at the top, and let it dry out for a while. Then water carefully. If this doesn't help, perhaps the pot is too big for the plant. Knock it out of the pot and examine the roots. If there seems to be a lot of soil in relation to the amount of root, put the plant in a smaller pot.

If the leaves of a plant are pale green, your plant may need more light. If only a few leaves are beginning to yellow, you may need plant food. If in spite of your attention, a plant does not recover, don't hesitate to throw it out. There is no use in cluttering up a good plant collection with sickly-looking plants.

CHAPTER 8

New Plants from Cuttings and Seeds

You can make new plants from old ones by cutting off a piece of stem, or sometimes a leaf, and placing it in a medium in which it can root. Other plants must be grown from seeds.

Cuttings provide a simple way of increasing the number of your favorite house plants. The method is simple. The easiest rooting medium to use is vermiculite or perlite. Both of these are sterile, hold lots of water, and permit the circulation of air, which is so necessary for root formation. Put the vermiculite or perlite in a bowl or pot and spray it with water until it is thoroughly wetted down.

The most convenient rooting box to use is a large plastic box. Punch a few drainage holes in the bottom with a heated ice pick. Then transfer enough of the moist vermiculite or perlite to it to make a two-inch layer.

Stem Cuttings

Use a sharp knife or scissors to make stem cuttings. Cut off a piece of stem about four inches long just below a node (where a leaf comes out of the stem). Trim off the leaves on the bottom two inches. Insert the cutting about one inch deep into the rooting medium. Cover the box with a hard plastic cover or with a thin sheet of plastic, and punch a few air holes in the lid. Put the box in a bright place, but not in direct sunlight. If the rooting medium was well wetted down to begin with, you probably won't have to water again until the cuttings are rooted. You can tell roots are formed when you see signs of growth in the stem. At this point the cutting should be transferred to a small pot containing soil. A new plant is born!

The easiest plants to root are the ivies, philodendron, begonias, geraniums, wandering Jew, and coleus. But try any and every plant whose number you want to increase. If roots don't form, try using the new plant hormones like Rootone, which induce root formation. Dip the cutting in the hormone powder before inserting it into the rooting medium.

Leaf Cuttings

New plants can sometimes be made from single leaves. This

stem cuttings

rooting box

is true of such plants as African violet, snake plant, kalanchoe, sedum, and many begonias. Select leaves that are neither too young nor too old. In the case of African violets and begonias, leave one inch of leaf stalk (petiole) and set the leaf stalk one

making a leaf cutting

half inch deep into the rooting medium. The leaves of some plants, however—kalanchoe and sedum, for example—have no petioles. Insert the base of these leaves into the planting medium. The long leaf of the snake plant can be cut up into pieces, each about two inches long, and each piece can be set halfway down into the rooting medium. It may take a few weeks for these leaf cuttings to root. When you see new clusters of tiny leaves you can move the new plants into small flowerpots.

Other Ways of Multiplying Plants

Some house plants, such as the strawberry plant, produce runners. The spider plant and the strawberry begonia produce small plantlets along runners that shoot out from the parent plant. These little plants can be cut off and planted in pots.

Some plants form several clumps in one pot, and these can

multiplying plants

simply be separated and potted. You can do this with the multiple clumps of African violet, snake plant, some begonias, ferns, etc. First water the plant. Then knock it out of the pot. If the clumps are tightly packed, use a knife to cut through and separate them. See that each piece has a fair amount of roots attached to it. Pot each piece in a container just big enough to hold the roots without crowding.

From Seeds

A lot of unusual and lovely plants cannot be bought, because there is little demand for them. You can add these to your collection by growing them from seed. Don't try this unless you have a bright sunny window in which to place your seed containers. In poor light, seedlings will be weak and spindly.

Directions for growing seeds indoors used to be very complicated, because ways of sterilizing soil by boiling and baking had to be explained in order to avoid damping-off—the worst hazard of growing seedlings indoors. Damping-off is a fungus disease that attacks the stems of young seedlings where they emerge from the earth and causes them to rot. Whole pans of seedlings can topple over in a few days as the result of this disease.

Today we have sterile packaged soils free of the fungus that causes the trouble. We have sterile vermiculite and perlite, too, which are wonderful for starting seeds. Any shallow containers will do, provided there are drainage holes in the bottom. Heavy aluminum foil containers, in which many of our frozen foods and cakes are sold, make excellent seed flats if they are about two inches high and if holes are punched in the bottom to allow excess water to drain off.

Wet the vermiculite or perlite in a separate dish until it is thoroughly moist. Fill the aluminum container to within a half inch of the top. Sow the seed on the surface and then cover the seeds with a layer equal to their own thickness. If you want just a few plants, sow only a few seeds. There is no point in sowing a whole package of seed and ending up with fifty new plants you have no room for.

Punch a few holes in a piece of Saran Wrap and cover the container with it. Usually no additional watering is necessary until the seeds sprout. When you do water, spray the surface lightly—just enough to keep the medium moist but not soaking wet. Remove the plastic cover when the plants are above ground, and keep the container in a sunny place.

When the seedlings have two pairs of leaves, they can be separated and transplanted into small flowerpots. Lift up the plant gently with a stick or pencil, and lower the roots into holes made in the soil of the pots. Put the young plant far enough down so that its first pair of leaves is flush with the soil, then firm the soil around it. Keep a newly transplanted seedling out of direct sunlight for a few days. Then put it with the rest of your house-plant collection.

transplanting a seedling

CHAPTER 9

Indoor Flowers from Bulbs

One of the delights of indoor gardening is to bring bulbs to flower in the dreary, dark winter months.

A bulb is surrounded by fleshy leaves. The flower bud is there inside the bulb when you buy it. All you really add in the process of bringing it to flower is water. If a bulb was not treated properly the year before, or if it is too small, it might not have a flower bud inside. This is the major cause of disappointment with bulbs. Therefore, be sure to buy good bulbs from reputable dealers.

The Easy Ones

The easiest bulbs to grow indoors are "tender" bulbs—those that do not require a cold-storage treatment before they flower. In fact, they are called tender because they freeze when subjected to low temperatures.

Narcissus indoor type bulbs come in three varieties: paper-white narcissus, yellow narcissus *(soeil d'or)*, and Chinese sacred lily, (a narcissus in spite of its name). The white flowers of the paper whites, the white and gold Chinese sacred lilies, and the yellow and orange *soleil d'ors* are all delicate and fragrant. Any one of these can be planted in a shallow container with pebbles, vermiculite, or perlite. Arrange the bulbs upright on a layer of the planting medium in small groups, so that they almost but don't quite touch each other. Fill in the spaces around them, allowing the top half of the bulbs to protrude above the surface. Add water and place the dish in a sunny window. A temperature of sixty to sixty-five degrees is best, so pick the coolest window in the house.

Amaryllis is another easy-to-grow bulb. The bulbs are rather expensive, but the tremendous, brilliant flowers that emerge from the bulb are worth seeing, and you can save the bulb from year to year. The bulbs can be bought and planted from November to March. Plant in a pot one inch larger than the bulb diameter. Set the bulb so that the upper half of it shows above the surface of the soil. Water the soil well after potting,

narcissus

amaryllis

crocus

lily-of-the-valley pips

and then do not water again until the bud comes out of the bulb. Then water it sparingly until the big fat flower bud pushes its way upward and bursts into bloom. When leaves appear, water freely. Keep the plant in a warm, well-lighted place. If you want to save the bulb, keep watering and fertilizing the plant during the period of leaf growth, because that is the time when new food for next year's flower bud is produced.

The autumn crocus is the easiest of all to grow. It will flower without even being potted. Plant these bulbs in shallow bowls with pebbles, vermiculite, or perlite. Add water and set the bowl in a window with light.

Lily-of-the-valley pips are not really bulbs, but they respond to the same treatment. They are pieces of root with buds at the top. The roots may be trimmed to fit the size of your bowl. These pips have already been given a cold-storage treatment by the time you buy them. Place the pips in an upright position in a bowl and pack vermiculite or perlite around the roots. Allow the buds to extend above the surface of the soil. Add water and keep in a warm, shady place until the leaves are four inches high. Then move to a bright light but not to direct sunlight. The flowers appear in three to four weeks.

Hardy Bulbs

The hardy bulbs, like tulips, hyacinths, spring crocuses, and daffodils, can be made to flower in the house in winter, but their culture is difficult because they have to go through a cold-storage treatment for two to three months. If you have a cold cellar, these bulbs can be planted in pots in September or October and kept there until the pots are filled with roots. Then bring them into the light and warmth. If your refrigerator is big enough to hold one pot of bulbs for two to three months, you will get the same result—the good mass of roots necessary to the further growth of these plants.

For beginners I would recommend leaving these hardy bulbs to the professional growers, and buying a potful at the florist's when they are blooming.

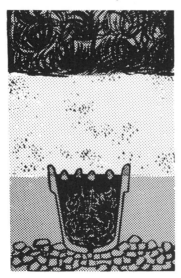

Roots of bulbs fill pots in cold storage.

bulbs ready to be brought in

CHAPTER 10

Adventures with House Plants

If you grow house plants, you are directly connected with the great field of plant research. Every day new things are being discovered in plant laboratories. It is exciting to follow the new developments and to find out about the problems still to be solved. Although we know many of the factors that control the development of a plant, much remains to be learned.

Plant research has a very practical relation to every grower of house plants. Many new plant chemicals quickly find their way to seed stores, florists, and nurseries. You can buy these new products and do some experimenting on your own.

The discovery of plant growth hormones was a milestone in plant research. The growing tips of leaves, stems, roots, and buds were shown to produce chemical substances called auxins. These hormones act like the well-known ones in the bodies of animals in one respect—they are produced in one part of the organism and affect a process in another part. They are chemical messengers that co-ordinate the growth of root, stem, and leaves. Tiny amounts of the auxins produce powerful effects on the growth of plants. They can make plant cells divide and lengthen. They can speed up the formation of roots on cuttings. They can prevent the growth of side buds. They can cause fruits to form from flowers that are not pollinated. They can affect flowering. These auxins were isolated from plants, and their chemical structure was studied. Soon after, synthetic compounds similar to the ones that naturally occur in plants were developed. Many of these are used today by gardeners, outdoors and indoors.

The indoor gardener can now understand why cutting off the top bud of a plant makes it more compact and bushy. The hormone produced by the top bud moves down and prevents the side buds from growing out. When the top bud is pinched off, the hormone stops being formed, and side buds develop into branches.

He can also understand why it is that plants in a window bend toward the light. Light causes the displacement of hormone in plants, so that there is more hormone on the shady side of the stem than on the sunny side. The hormone on the shady side makes the cells there grow more rapidly, and so the plant bends over toward the light.

The most popular use of hormones has been to induce roots on cuttings. Hormones speed up the formation of roots and increase their number and size as well. They are not usually necessary for ordinary house-plant cuttings. But plants that are difficult to root will respond to a hormone treatment. It will be interesting for you to experiment with these hormones to see for yourself whether they make any difference in the rooting of cuttings. They are on the market in the form of Rootone, Hormodin, etc., usually in powder form. Just dip the bottom end of the cuttings into the hormone powder before you put them in a rooting box. To do a real experiment, you will have to compare several cuttings that have been dipped into hormone powder with several cuttings that have not been dipped. This last group will be your control group. In order to discover the effect of the hormone, you must have this untreated group to compare with the treated group.

There is a lot of evidence that there is a flower-producing hormone in plants. It has been called florigen, but it has not yet been isolated. It is, however, a real possibility that florigen will be isolated and put to use in the near future.

There are fruit-set hormones—commercial preparations that are sold under the names Fruitone, Blossom-set, etc. Ordinarily, fruit can form only after flowers are pollinated by insects, wind, or other means. But these new hormones trigger the change of ovary to fruit, skipping the pollination step. They are widely used on tomatoes to cause the setting of fruit early in the season. They are also being used on other fruits and vegetables, where unfavorable conditions prevent the flowers from being pollinated. Not much has been done with these hormones on house plants, however. Try these new products yourself. Experiment to see whether they help form fruits on such plants as the Jerusalem cherry, the dwarf orange, the grapefruit, and the lemon. Follow the manufacturer's directions carefully.

For a while vitamin B1 was making the headlines as a great promoter of plant growth. Further research showed these claims to be untrue, although vitamins *are* manufactured by green plants. In fact, green plants are our great natural source of most vitamins. But although vitamins play a role in the growth of plants, plant organs seem to manufacture enough vitamins to supply their own needs. No additional vitamins are necessary.

A real Jack-and-the-Beanstalk chemical made newspaper headlines last year. The new substance was named gibberellin, after the fungus Gibberella, which causes a rice disease in Japan. This disease was called "foolish seedling disease," because the diseased plants grow "foolishly" taller than normal ones. The Japanese discovered and isolated the active substance

gibberellin experiment

untreated   treated

produced by this fungus and named it gibberellin. It seemed to have growth-regulating properties, like the auxins. Nobody outside of Japan paid much attention to gibberellin until 1950, when a group of American and English scientists started a series of studies. Interest in it spread from these groups, and recently the United States Department of Agriculture did an elaborate series of tests on many kinds of plants.

All plants normally possess gibberellin, just as they possess the other growth substances. When plants are treated with gibberellin, however, dramatic changes may occur. It doubles the height of some plants. The stems of citrus trees lengthen until they are more than six times normal size. When plants like dahlias, Shasta daisies, and African violets are treated with it, they blossom sooner than untreated plants. It makes biennials (plants that bloom only once in two years) flower the first year. It helps germination in some kinds of seeds.

There are many commercial preparations of gibberellin now on sale. Most of the work on it, however, has been done on field and crop plants. Very little has been done on house plants, so there is a chance for you to do some experimenting of your own.

Many new discoveries are constantly being made. Watch the newspaper and the garden and flower magazines for information about new plant products you can have fun with.

Guide to the Culture of Some Common House Plants

The plants are listed alphabetically by their popular names, except where there is no popular name, or where the technical name is also widely used.

African evergreen *(Syngonium podophyllum or Nephthytis)*: See page 44

African violet *(Saintpaulia ionantha)*: Requires plenty of light but not direct burning sun, an evenly moist soil, high humidity, and steady temperature between sixty and seventy degrees. Use water at room temperature. Special soils with high humus content are available. When crowns multiply and fill pot, divide and repot.

Aloe: See *Succulents,* page 48.

Amaryllis *(Hippeastrum hybridum)*: See *Bulbs,* pages 81-82.

Apostle plant *(Marica* species): Keep in small pots in sunny window. Water generously.

Asparagus fern *(Asparagus* species): Requires rich soil, liberal fertilizer, cool temperature, sunlight, lots of water, and regular spraying of foliage.

Aspidistra: See *Cast-iron plant,* page 39.

Australian umbrella tree *(Schefflera actinophylla)*: See page 43.

Autumn Crocus *(Colchicum autumnale)*: See page 83.

Baby tears *(Helxine soleirolii)*: Requires cool temperature, bright light but not direct sunlight, an evenly moist soil, and high humidity.

Begonias: Require good drainage, loose soil rich in humus, soil kept evenly moist, high humidity (spray leaves often), sunshine in winter, and light shade the other seasons. There are thousands of varieties, with interesting leaf shapes and lovely flowers.

Billbergia: See *Bromeliads,* page 49.

Bryophyllum: See *Succulents,* page 48.

Cactus: See page 45.

Caladium *(Caladium bicolor):* Grow from tubers which may be started in February or March. Plant in shallow box. Place a half inch deep in vermiculite. When growth starts, plant each of the tubers in a three-inch pot. Use soil rich in humus. Keep in a warm, bright place out of direct sunlight. Water freely. In fall, when leaves die down, allow soil to dry out and store pots in warm, dry place for a few months. Then repot.

Cast-iron plant *(Aspidistra elatior):* See page 39.

Chinese evergreen *(Aglaonema* species): See page 40.

Christmas cactus *(Zygocactus truncatus):* Keep at a cool temperature between fifty-five and sixty-five degrees. Give bright light but not direct sunshine, humidity, and well-drained soil rich in humus. In the fall keep soil on the dry side until flower buds form.

Citrus: Orange, lemon, and grapefruit plants need soil rich in humus, full sun, cool temperature, and frequent spraying of foliage with water.

Coleus: Requires lots of water, sunlight, and frequent pinching back. Watch out for mealy bugs.

Corn plant *(Dracaena fragrans)*: See page 45.

Crocus: See *Bulbs,* page 84.

Croton *(Codiaeum* species): Requires high temperature, high humidity, and sunny position.

Crown of thorns *(Euphorbia splendens)*: See Succulents, page 48.

Cyclamen *(Cyclamen indicum)*: Gift plant that should be discarded after flowering unless you have a cool greenhouse.

Daffodils *(Narcissus* species): See *Bulbs,* page 84.

Dieffenbachia: See *Dumb cane,* page 45.

Dracaena: See *Corn plant,* page 45.

Dumb cane *(Dieffenbachia* species): See page 45.

Echeveria: See *Succulents,* page 48.

English ivy *(Hedera helix)*: See page 42.

Fatshedera: See page 44.

Ferns: Require shade, moist soil rich in humus, frequent spraying of leaves with water.

Ficus: See *Rubber plant,* page 39.

Fuchsia: Requires loose soil rich in humus, lots of water, moist atmosphere, partial shade, and cool temperature.

Gardenia: Requires warm, moist atmosphere, sunny position, frequent spraying of leaves with water. Soil should be rich in humus and kept constantly moist.

Geranium *(Pelargonium* species): Requires sunlight, soil kept on dry side, cool temperature, regular fertilizing when buds forming, frequent pinching back.

Gloxinia *(Sinningia speciosa)*: Requires soil that is rich in humus and kept evenly moist, bright light but not direct sunlight, temperatures between sixty and seventy degrees, moist atmosphere. Start tubers in March, plant half inch deep in moist vermiculite. When growth shows, transfer each tuber into a separate small pot. Repot when necessary. In the fall, reduce water, keep the tubers dry in the pots till spring, then repot.

Grapefruit: See *Citrus.*

Grape ivy *(Cissus rhombifolia):* See page 42.

Hen and chickens *(Encheneria* species): See *Succulents,* page 48.

Hyacinth *(Hyacinthus* species): See *Bulbs,* page 84.

Ivy: See page 42.

Jade plant *(Crassula argentea):* See *Succulents,* page 48.

Jerusalem cherry *(Solanum pseudocapsicum):* Requires cool situation, plenty of sun, lots of water. Fruits are poisonous.

Kalanchoe: See *Succulents,* page 48.

Lemon: See *Citrus.*

Live-forever *(Sedum* species): See *Succulents,* page 48.

Monstera: See *Swiss cheese plant,* page 41.

Morning-glory *(Ipomoea* species): Requires full sunlight and moist atmosphere.

Narcissus: See *Bulbs,* page 81.

Nephythytis *(Syngonium podophyllum):* See *African evergreen,* page 44.

Orange: See *Citrus.*

Palms: Require moist soil, bright light but not strong sunlight, frequent spraying of foliage.

Pandanus: See *Screw pine,* page 43.

Peperomia: Requires warm temperature, moist atmosphere, frequent spraying of leaves, bright light but not direct sunlight.

Philodendron: See page 40.

Pickaback plant *(Tolmiea menziesi)*: Requires lots of water, a bright light out of direct sunlight, and cool temperatures. New plantlets form where the leaf meets the stem. These can be separated and put in pots.

Poinsettia *(Euphorbia pulcherrimma)*: Put this gift plant away after it loses flowers and leaves and keep it in a cool cellar in the dried-out soil. In the spring, cut the stems back to about six inches, repot in new soil, and give the plant plenty of water and sunshine. Poinsettia requires twelve hours of darkness per day to flower. Do not keep it in a lighted room at night.

Prayer plant *(Maranta leuconeura)*: Requires warm, moist atmosphere, no direct sunlight. Good for use in terrariums.

Primrose *(Primula* species)*: Gift plant that should be kept in a cool, shady place, constantly moist.

Rubber plant *(Ficus* species)*: See page 39.

Sansevieria: See *Snake plant,* page 38.

Screw pine *(Pandanus* species)*: See page 43.

Sedum: See *Succulents,* page 48.

Snake plant *(Sansevieria* species)*: See page 38.

Spider plant *(Chlorophytum elatum)*: See page 38.

Succulents: See page 47.

Swiss cheese plant *(Monstera deliciosa)*: See page 41.

95

Tradescantia. See *Wandering Jew, page 43.*
Tulip (*Tulipa* species): See *Bulbs,* page 84.
Wandering Jew (*Tradescantia* species): See page 43.

Where to Buy House Plants and Supplies

To begin with, find your plants in five-and-tens, florists, or nearby greenhouses and nurseries. After a while you might want to build up your collection with more unusual plants. Then you can consult the advertisements in garden and flower magazines and in newspapers to find mail-order places that specialize in different types of plants.

You can buy ingredients for soil mixtures at five-and-tens, seed and hardware stores, supermarkets, florist shops, and nurseries. Vermiculite is often sold under the trade names Terra-Lite or Mica-Gro. Perlite is sold as Pelonex.

Some of the new house-plant pressurized aerosol bombs that control insect pests are called Acme, Antrol, Bostwick, D-X, Killogen, and Red Arrow.

Plant chemicals you might want to experiment with can be ordered from flower catalogues or from such special sources as:

Romaine B. Ware, Canby, Oregon

Princeton Phytochemicals, Inc., Box 7, Princeton Junction, N. J.

General Biological Supply House, 761-3 East 69th Place,
Chicago 37, Illinois